Piggy yells, "Lemonade for sale!"

Piggy drinks some lemonade.

Piggy yells, "Lemonade for sale!"

Piggy drinks more lemonade.

Piggy yells, "LEMONADE FOR SALE!"

Piggy drinks MORE lemonade.

Dad says, "Lemonade, please."

Piggy says, "Oops, all gone."